Building Houses

Wright Group

The McGraw-Hill Companies

We **built** houses
for our art project.
Do you like them?

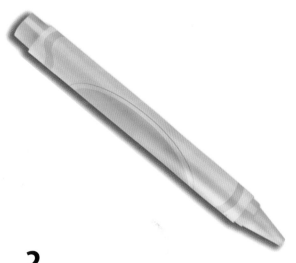

3

My **house** has
one red roof.
How do you like it?

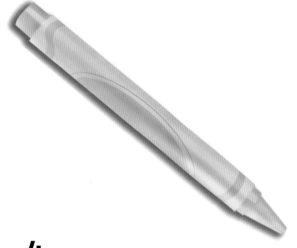

My house has
two purple doors.
How do you like it?

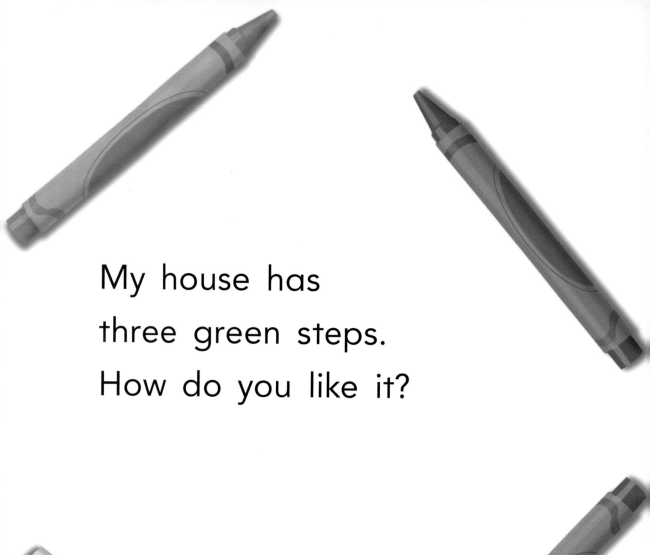

My house has
three green steps.
How do you like it?

9

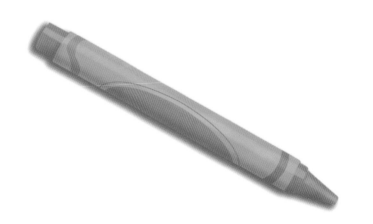

My house has
four pink windows.
I wish more houses
were pink!

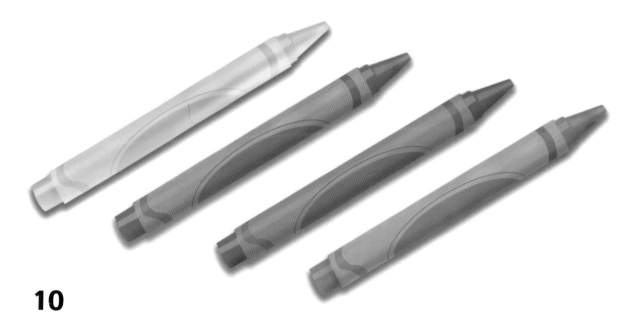

Focus Question

What kinds of homes are there?

Draw a picture of a home that you read about.

12